embrace your inner

BADASS

Companion Workbook

KALI WILLIAMS

BRAZEN
INK
PRESS

Published by Brazen Ink
Presswww.BrazenInkPress.com
San Jose, CA

Cover design by Hannah Portello-Swagel
Book design by Hannah Portello-Swagel and Kali Williams

ISBN: 978-1-7340322-2-2

Printed in the United States of America

"When I dare to be powerful, to use my strength in the service of my vision, then it becomes less and less important whether I am afraid."
--Audre Lorde

CONTENTS

GETTING STARTED

Start Here... 1

How to Get the Most Out of Journaling................................. 2

Where Are You now?... 5

Future-Self Visualization... 11

What's in a Word? Negative and Positive Words for Women.... 12

What Does the Word "Bitch" Mean to You?......................... 17

How is the Bitch Stigma Impacting You?............................. 19

Bitch Privilege and Intersectional Identities..................... 32

How Does Your Identity Impact Your Behavior?.............. 34

THE MIRROR MATRIX

Introducing the Mirror Matrix + Grid of Traits................ 35

Looking in the Mirror... 37

The Mirror Matrix Archetype Profiles................................. 39

Toxic Bitch Archetypes... 40

Bold Badass Archetypes.. 47

YOUR ARCHETYPES

Your Five Archetypes... 72

Which Badass or Bitch (Or Both) Are You?....................... 74

Which Bitches and Badasses Do You Know?.................... 76

Priority Assessment Tool.. 77

Getting Comfortable with Discomfort................................. 80

Getting to Know Your Inner Doomsday Machine.............. 84

Sensory Deprivation as a Tool for Focus............................ 88

Create Personal Affirmations... 91

YOUR NETWORK

Mutual Admiration Society.. 93

Assessing Your Network.. 95

Toxic Relationships.. 98

Build Your Network.. 101

CONTENTS

TOOLS & EXERCISES

Tap Into Your Sensory Sparks 102

Your Power Song and Kickass Playlist 105

Role-play Difficult Conversations 106

Field Research 108

Practice Being a Badass 110

How Do You Speak Up and Set Boundaries? 111

Building a Reward System 113

Incentivizing Confidence 114

Keep Track for a Month 115

YOUR MOST CONFIDENT SELF

Envisioning Your Most Confident Self 119

Who Inspires You? 125

Most Confident Self Profile 126

Build a Vision Board 128

Reflect on Miscommunications 129

Just Say No 130

Identifying Your Soft Language Habits 131

Take a Sorry Detox 133

Speak With Strength 134

Write Stronger Emails 135

Speak with Authority 137

MANSPLAINING & CONVERSATIONAL BULLDOZING

Mansplaining and Conversational Bulldozing 138

Tips and Scripts to Stop Mansplainers and Conversational Bulldozers ... 141

Practice Strategic Interrupting 142

Protect Your Personal Space 144

Get Big 145

FINAL THOUGHTS & RESOURCES

Where Are You Now? 147

Recommended Reading 149

------------------- START HERE -------------------

This workbook is meant to be a companion to the book Ditch the Bitch Stigma: Embrace Your Inner Badass, my guide for women to build the confidence they need to set boundaries, ask for what they want, and excel in a male-dominated world—developed from the perspective of my own unique expertise as a kink coach and former professional dominatrix.

The book itself dives deep into each of these concepts, while this workbook gives you space to reflect, respond, and plan. It's perfect to use as you're reading the book to help you put ideas into action in your life. Basically, it's a DIY version of my coaching program and immersive retreat.

There are two main components to this workbook: "Go Deeper" and "Take Action." The "Go Deeper" sections consist of open-ended questions designed to make you think carefully and critically about your habits, goals, anxieties, and strengths. The "Take Action" sections offer exercises to help you turn your reflections into actions.

If you're working through the book and accompanying activities at home, give yourself time to sit and respond to the Go Deeper questions and to consider your answers without feeling rushed. There's no "right" answer to any of these questions; it's all about giving you space to reflect on your experiences and goals. Writing out your thoughts can lead to profound personal insights.

If you can't relate to a question, feel free to reword it or skip it. You can always come back to it later. And if a question inspires other related (or unrelated) reflections, don't hold back! Feel free to use the space for your own questions and thoughts, too.

When you come to the "Take Action" sections, remember that you might need to do the exercises multiple times in order to get comfortable with what they're trying to teach you. Take the practice at your own pace, but don't let too much time pass in between your efforts, because you'll build more momentum and more resilience if you keep at it consistently.

Achieving the life and freedom you desire will require a combination of introspection and action, and this workbook will support you in that process.

You can work through these exercises and activities any way that makes sense to you. You can go through them methodically in the order they're written, or you can jump around to the sections that resonate most at any given time. Feel free to get creative! Use different-colored pens, highlighters, or anything that will make this book as unique as you are.

~ Kali

HOW TO MAKE THE MOST OUT OF JOURNALING

The "Go Deeper" sections of this workbook function like a journal, giving you the space and inspiration to really reflect on your past, where you are now, what you hope for the future, and how you plan to make it happen. With that in mind, I wanted to take a moment before we jump in to offer a few journaling tips to help you make the most of these exercises.

I've been a lifelong journaler. In fact, I still have my journals from when I was nine and every journal I've ever written in since. I have goal journals, dream journals, scrapbook and art journals, and even spirituality journals. So you could say I know a thing or two about writing your way to self-discovery.

Below, you'll find my favorite tips to get the most out of your journaling experience.

1

Journaling is a habit, and like any habit, you need to do it often enough for it to become second nature. Make space for it in your life. You don't need that much time—even five to ten minutes goes a long way. You can even set a daily reminder alarm on your phone so you don't forget.

2

There's no single "right" way to journal. Some folks find it helpful to write at a set time every day, like in the morning with your tea or coffee, or at night before you go to bed. And if writing every day isn't feasible for you, that's ok! Write when the mood strikes or when you have some extra time or emotional bandwidth.

3

Use a pen that you like to write with. It may seem silly or small, but I actually look forward to using my pens (office supply nerd here!), and a pen I'm excited about can help tip the scales for whether I actually journal or not that day.

HOW TO MAKE THE MOST OUT OF JOURNALING

4

Try to do "stream of consciousness" writing, meaning that you don't edit as you go but you let your hand write exactly what your mind thinks. You're not trying to win any awards with this kind of writing; it's for your own self-reflection and knowledge. So let your thoughts go, and do your best to let go of your judgment of them.

5

If you're writing about an experience, don't feel obligated to write every detail down if that feels tedious or time-consuming. Feel free to write extensively or keep it simple and focus on the most important elements to reflect on.

6

You're welcome to write right in the workbook, and in fact, I encourage it. But if you run out of space in these pages, move your reflections to whatever medium you're most likely to actually use. If that's a note in your phone, great! If you want to use a luxe leather bound notebook, that's great, too! Frankly though, in my experience, when a journal is too expensive and fancy-shmancy, it can be tough to make yourself mar it with imperfect writing (even though that's the point!). Remember, the most important thing is that the medium makes it easier and more inviting for you to write.

7

The written word isn't the only way to express yourself! I'm a big fan of getting the old magazine collages out and adding scraps of bits and pieces of my life into my paper journals, even if they aren't technically "art" journals. If you have a digital diary instead, insert photos or screenshots to give it more visual interest.

8

If you use paper journals that are too big to carry everywhere with you, start a note on your phone where you can capture stray thoughts you can elaborate on when you have more time and focus. Or use voice-to-text to record yourself responding to journal prompts or random thoughts.

Remember, you aren't writing this for anyone else
—you're writing it for yourself!

LET'S GET STARTED!

GO DEEPER:
WHERE ARE YOU NOW?

Let's get this off to a solid start by making a commitment to work through this book and make changes in our lives. By putting this book into practice, we're making space to grow.

It's only when we look ahead and see the benefits of change that change becomes possible. We have to be willing to sit with the discomfort of transition and stay focused on exactly what we're going to get out of the change once we put it into practice. If we're operating on vague ideas like, "I'm gonna speak up more," those ideas are hard to commit to, as they're just too fuzzy.

Instead of limiting your goals to general ideas, quantify them. If we don't articulate exactly what we're chasing after, then we'll never know if we've achieved it or not. I want you to understand your what and your why. What do you want?

To be more outspoken
To set better boundaries
To expand your existing confidence

What else? These are all great ideas, but they're still just ideas. To turn these into real, achievable goals, you need to understand exactly what achieving them will look like. In what situations do you want to be more outspoken? With whom do you need to set boundaries? Why do you want to make these changes? What is going to change in your life as a result?

In the spirit of clarifying our goals and setting our intentions, I encourage you to take a look at where you are now and where you'd like to be in the future.

Take some time to answer the following questions on the following pages.

WHERE ARE YOU NOW?

What are some things you do well?

PERSONAL	PROFESSIONAL

6

WHERE ARE YOU NOW?

What are some things you need to work on improving?

PERSONAL	PROFESSIONAL

WHERE ARE YOU NOW?

What is important to you, and what do you value? Why?

PERSONAL	PROFESSIONAL

VALUE LIST

Our values are the fundamental beliefs that guide the way we live our everyday lives. When we fully understand what we value, we can make better decisions for ourselves.

Here are some examples to get you started on your own list.

Acceptance	Dependability	Health	Originality
Accomplishment	Discipline	Honesty	Power
Adaptability	Empathy	Hope	Productivity
Balance	Ethics	Independence	Professionalism
Bravery	Fairness	Innovation	Prosperity
Challenge	Family	Integrity	Security
Charity	Freedom	Intelligence	Self-Reliance
Comfort	Friendship	Joy	Sincerity
Community	Fun	Justice	Spirituality
Competence	Gratitude	Kindness	Stability
Creativity	Growth	Love	Success
Curiosity	Happiness	Loyalty	Wisdom

ADD YOUR OWN

WHERE ARE YOU NOW?

What changes do you hope to make as a result of reading the book and completing the reflections and challenges in this workbook?

FUTURE-SELF VISUALIZATION

Close your eyes and get settled. Take a few deep breaths.

Now imagine that it's five years in the future. Visualize the sights, sounds, smells, and emotions you aspire to, and describe your vision in as much detail as possible.

GO DEEPER:
WHAT'S IN A WORD?

Let's take a look at the negative or gendered other words that are used to describe (or insult) confident women.

Abrasive	Cold	Dramatic	Princess
Aggressive	Combative	High Maintenance	Pushy
Angry	Condescending	Intense	Rude
Ballbuster	Control Freak	Intimidating	Shrew
Bossy	Cunt	Militant	Shrill
Brusque	Demanding	Nag	Unapproachable
Calculating	Difficult	Overbearing	Unlikable

Write down all the associative words you can think of related to bitch.

WHAT'S IN A WORD?

Which of these words is most triggering for you?

_____

Why do you think that is?

_____

What did it trigger in you (anger, anxiety, frustration, sadness, what else)?

_____

WHAT'S IN A WORD?

Choose four words from page 12, and elaborate on your
feelings, experiences, and thoughts about each.

Word:

Feelings, Experiences and Thoughts:

_____

_____

_____

_____

Word:

Feelings, Experiences and Thoughts:

_____

_____

_____

_____

Word:

Feelings, Experiences and Thoughts:

_____

_____

_____

_____

Word:

Feelings, Experiences and Thoughts:

_____

_____

_____

_____

GO DEEPER:
WHAT'S IN A WORD?

Not everyone feels comfortable with the idea of "reclaiming" a negative word, and that's ok. There are plenty of other ways to identify and embrace your own unique strength and power.

Here are just a few to consider:

Authoritative	Daring	Leader	Self-Assured
Bold	Edgy	Maverick	Sincere
Brazen	Fearless	Memorable	Straightforward
Brilliant	Fierce	Outspoken	Tenacious
Candid	Forceful	Poised	Tough
Commanding	Formidable	Powerful	Unapologetic
Courageous	Free	Powerhouse	Vibrant

Add any other positive words you can think of that are used to describe women and then circle the ones you especially relate to or aspire to.

WHAT'S IN A WORD?

Choose four words from page 15, and elaborate on your feelings, experiences, and thoughts about each.

Word:

Feelings, Experiences and Thoughts:

_____
_____
_____
_____

Word:

Feelings, Experiences and Thoughts:

_____
_____
_____
_____

Word:

Feelings, Experiences and Thoughts:

_____
_____
_____
_____

Word:

Feelings, Experiences and Thoughts:

_____
_____
_____

WHAT DOES THE WORD "BITCH" MEAN TO YOU?

Language is very personal, so let's stop for a minute to figure out what the word "bitch" means to you.

Do you remember the first time you heard someone called a bitch?

Have you ever been called a bitch (or one of the derogatory words from the previous section)? What was the situation?

Which of your innate behaviors or actions are most often construed as bitchiness? How does that feel?

Describe a time when you worked hard to find that "just right" Goldilocks sweet spot. Were you successful? What were the ramifications?

GO DEEPER:
HOW IS THE BITCH STIGMA IMPACTING YOU?

As women, we're conditioned from birth to do everything we can to avoid seeming like a bitch. That conditioning has led to common coping mechanisms and avoidance behaviors women tend to use to either avoid or lean into "bitchiness." These include hyper-feminine presentation, uptalk and vocal fry, excessive perkiness, and emotional stoicism, among others.

Do any of the coping mechanisms mentioned in the book
stand out as relatable to you?

What coping mechanisms do you use to avoid the Bitch Stigma in your professional or personal interactions?

GO DEEPER:
HOW IS THE BITCH STIGMA IMPACTING YOU?

Have you ever been told that you have Resting Bitch Face or Resting Bitch Tone? If so, what do you say to people who call you out for it?

_____
_____
_____
_____
_____
_____
_____
_____

How has the Bitch Stigma impacted the way you interact with the world? What have you learned about the expectations of your behavior?

_____
_____
_____
_____
_____
_____
_____
_____

Set a timer to write for twenty minutes, and on the following pages, list every example or situation you can think of in which the Bitch Stigma has prevented you from communicating with strength or from reaching your goals at work, with friends, family, and romantic partners, as well as your general safety.

Then, on the opposite side of the page, choose one or two of the most impactful experiences you listed, and write out how you would've handled it differently if you weren't being impacted by the Bitch Stigma.

How would you communicate differently?

What would you have done differently?

What do you think the response would've been if you'd handled it that way?

List every example or situation you can think of in your work life in which the Bitch Stigma is preventing you from communicating with strength or reaching your goals.

Choose one or two of work situations you've listed. Write how you would've handled the situation if you weren't being impacted by the Bitch Stigma.

How would you communicate differently? How would you have handled it differently?
What do you think the response would've been if you'd handled it that way?

_____

_____

_____

_____

_____

_____

_____

_____

_____

_____

_____

_____

_____

_____

_____

_____

_____

List every example or situation you can think of in your family life in which the Bitch Stigma is preventing you from communicating with strength or reaching your goals.

FAMILY

Choose one or two of the family situations you've listed.
Write how you would've handled the situation if you weren't
being impacted by the Bitch Stigma.

How would you communicate differently? How would you have handled it differently?
What do you think the response would've been if you'd handled it that way?

FRIENDS

List every example or situation you can think of with your friends in which the Bitch Stigma is preventing you from communicating with strength or reaching your goals.

Choose one or two of the situations you've listed. Write how you would've handled the situation if you weren't being impacted by the Bitch Stigma.

How would you communicate differently? How would you have handled it differently?
What do you think the response would've been if you'd handled it that way?

ROMANTIC PARTNERS

List every example or situation you can think of with your current or previous romantic partner(s) in which the Bitch Stigma is preventing you from communicating with strength or reaching your goals.

ROMANTIC PARTNERS

Choose one or two of the situations you've listed. Write how you would've handled the situation if you weren't being impacted by the Bitch Stigma.

How would you communicate differently? How would you have handled it differently?
What do you think the response would've been if you'd handled it that way?

SAFETY

List every example or situation you can think of in which
the Bitch Stigma put your safety at risk.

SAFETY

Choose one or two of the safety situations you've listed.
Write how you would've handled the situation if you weren't
being impacted by the Bitch Stigma.

How would you communicate differently? How would you have handled it differently?
What do you think the response would've been if you'd handled it that way?

GO DEEPER:
BITCH PRIVILEGE &
INTERSECTIONAL IDENTITIES

Not all women are treated equally. There are a lot of factors that impact how our behavior is received and perceived.

The Bitch Stigma is rooted in gender, but there are always additional layers to it based on obvious characteristics of our personal presentations. And it's not just about how we personally identify, but how other people see us.

These intersectional identities create extra layers of obstacles for women fighting to overcome biases outside of gender. It's important to note that there are a number of identities that can compound the bias against women. This list is not exhaustive; I encourage you to add any other identity markers that affect you and/or the people in your life.

Age

Beauty Standards / Conventional Attractiveness

Being Transgender or Nonbinary

Body Type

Class / Financial Status

Disability

Education Level

English as a Second Language

Gender Presentation

Job Title / Seniority

Neurodivergency

Parenthood

Perceived Sexual Orientation

Perceived Sexual Promiscuity / Prudishness

Race / Ethnicity

Religion

Sexual Orientation

Shy / Outgoing

BITCH PRIVILEGE & INTERSECTIONAL IDENTITIES

On the following page, write about how any of the identities you possess have affected the way others perceive your behavior.

Have they led to privilege or marginalization?
And how has that impacted your ability to assert yourself?
What about identities you don't possess?
How might your identities impact your friends, relatives, or colleagues?

Identity:

Experience:

→ _____

_____

_____

→ _____

_____

_____

→ _____

_____

_____

→ _____

_____

_____

→ _____

_____

_____

GO DEEPER:
HOW DOES YOUR IDENTITY IMPACT YOUR BEHAVIOR?

What influence does your background play in your communication style and your ability to set boundaries or otherwise put yourself first?

How does your personality come into play?

In what ways are you privileged, and how can you use that privilege to lift both yourself and others?

INTRODUCING
THE MIRROR MATRIX

I've created a system of archetypes that I call the Mirror Matrix to help you recognize the different ways confidence presents itself and to differentiate between toxic and healthy bitch behavior.

The Mirror Matrix includes the full spectrum of attitudes—both Toxic Bitches who exhibit negative, undesirable behaviors and Bold Badasses who are confident and independent women. No matter where you fall on any given day or in any given situation, it's all about how you see yourself in the mirror.

The Mirror Matrix is meant as a guide, to give you a tool along with language you can use to differentiate between Toxic and Bold behavior—and to help you get acquainted with your own self-perception.

There are nine archetypes total,
including three Toxic Bitches and six Bold Badasses.

The grid introduces you to each archetype
on its own spectrum of intensity.

THE MIRROR MATRIX

ADVOCATE

Polite, Tactful, Formal
Principled
Chooses Her Battles
Honest, Straightforward
Academic
Integrity-Driven
Otherwise Mild-Mannered
Does the "Right Thing" Even
When it's the Hard Thing

WARRIOR

Fierce
Tireless/Relentless
Vigilant
Passionate
Intensely Convicted
Persistent/Perseverant
Committed to a Cause
Action-Driven
Brave/Proud
Fiercely Loyal

FANATIC

Opinion Tornado
Relentless
Unmovable
Single-focus/Fixated
Demanding
Militant
Rigid/Inflexible
Aggressive/Volatile
Underhanded/Manipulative
Rooted in a belief system

QUEEN

Enigmatic
Dignified
Aloof, Remote
Self-Contained
Woman of Few Words
Diplomatic
Observant
Contemplative
Imposing

BOSS

Competent, Skillful
In Charge
Hierarchal
Collaborative
Brusque/No-Nonsense
Enforces Protocols
Accomplished
Action-Driven
Authoritative
Assumes Leadership Easily

STEAMROLLER

Condescending
Overbearing
Superiority Complex/Narcissism
Competitive
Micro-Manager
Oblivious
Dismissive
Pompous
Testy/Snappy
Insensitive
Doesn't listen

REBEL

Blunt
Self-Possessed
Trailblazing/Pioneering
Charming
Influential
Rebellious
Edgy
Outspoken

ROGUE

Unorthodox
Radical/Non-Conformist
Sharp-Tongued/Snarky
Truth-Teller
Anti-Establishment
Anti-Authority
Takes No Prisoners
Unapologetic
Hard-nosed

FANATIC

Rude/Catty
Arrogant
Manipulative
Hardened
Domineering
Temperamental
Secretive
Demeaning
Uses Humiliation

GO DEEPER:
LOOKING IN THE MIRROR

You'll notice the first two columns in the grid include Bold Badasses, and the third includes Toxic Bitches.

A number of factors go into determining whether someone is being toxic or bold, so how can you tell the difference in your own "bitchy" behavior? All it takes is a little self-reflection.

Intention does matter, especially when others are likely to view our actions through the lens of the Bitch Stigma and general sexist stereotypes. So take a look at what you're trying to do and whether your intention lines up with your integrity. Most of us know when we're being toxic, even if we won't admit it out loud.

Here are some questions you can ask yourself:

What are you attempting to accomplish?

What are you trying to communicate?

Are your actions in line with your intentions?

Are you lashing out about something that has made you angry, frustrated, disappointed, annoyed, jealous, or something else?

Does the person you're communicating with potentially have some conscious or unconscious biases that is influencing their perception?

GO DEEPER:
LOOKING IN THE MIRROR

You can't stop at intention, though, because impact may matter, too, depending on the situation.

Especially if you feel conflict brewing with someone important in your life, then your intention can be overwhelmed by your impact.

We'll go deeper into this in a later reflection, but you can start with these questions:

Are your actions or behavior actually harmful to the other person?

Does the person have a double standard for behavior they allow from other people, especially men?

Who is this person in your life?

Does their opinion matter? Why?

THE MIRROR MATRIX
ARCHETYPE PROFILES

In the coming pages, we'll look at in-depth profiles of each archetype.

As you read through them, you'll likely notice yourself identifying with one or more, and that's great. You can think of them as equally strong components of your personality, or you can think of them as pieces of a different kind of astrological chart—maybe you're a Queen with Steamroller rising. There's no "right way" to relate to these archetypes. After all, the Mirror Matrix all about you.

Keep these five profiles in mind as you read:

CORE \ SECONDARY \ ASPIRATIONAL \ SITUATIONAL \ TOXIC

The following pages have plenty of room for you to dig deeper into each archetype, including a description, standard motto, personality traits, pop culture examples, and affirmations for each kind of badass. There's also information about the challenges each archetype commonly faces and the toxic potential for each type of badass.

You'll also find a page to brainstorm responses to difficult situations in each style of badass and a couple of blank pages for you to doodle and add any other notes you observe about each archetype.

As you read, you'll likely think of women you know who fit each one.

There's a chart where you can jot down names of people in your circle who fit each archetype on page 76, but as you read the profiles feel free to record any other characteristics that come to mind for the different kinds of badass and toxic bitches.

TOXIC
BITCH
ARCHETYPES

FANATIC

The Fanatic has strong opinions and wants everyone to know it. Her insistence on being correct is an obstacle to having a mutually respectful conversation, and she can be incredibly dogmatic. She speaks with intensity and relentlessness and could easily be described as an "opinion tornado."

The Fanatic is overly defensive and belittles other people's experiences and opinions if they don't line up with her own. She might have "control freak" tendencies and have a hard time sharing power. The Fanatic is a woman of extremes: she'll either ice you out and give you the cold shoulder or she'll explode in a fiery rage. She can be confrontational, and she might be a screamer when she gets angry.

---- **MOTTO** ----

"I'm right, and that's just a fact."

---- **TRAITS** ----

Opinion tornado
Relentless
Unmovable
Single-focus/Fixated

Demanding
Militant
Opinionated/loud

Rigid/Inflexible
Aggressive/Volatile
Underhanded/Manipulative
Rooted in a belief system

POP CULTURE

Cersei Lannister (Game of Thrones)
Claire Underwood (House of Cards)
Sherry Palmer (24)

Jeanine Pirro (Entertainer)
Valerie Solanas (Radical Feminist)
Rosanne Barr (Actress)

CHALLENGES

Off-put doesn't even begin to describe how others feel when the Fanatic gets going about her most passionate beliefs. It seems nearly impossible for others to discuss or debate ideas because of her refusal to even acknowledge other people's perspectives or opinions.

NOTES

FANATIC

STEAMROLLER

The Steamroller is overbearing and impatient and has a major superiority complex, though she might not admit it. She has no need to hear your opinion because hers is obviously so much better. She can often be a micromanager who doesn't trust others to accomplish what she is able to do herself. Her tone is frequently bossy, and if she's in a managerial position she likes to remind her team who's in charge.

She's highly competitive and can undermine those around her. She might see herself as someone who has high standards, but the way she upholds those standards comes across as rigidity and unwillingness to compromise. She believes in brutal honesty, with an emphasis on the "brutal." She's not always malicious, but her behavior is toxic anyway.

MOTTO

"As I was saying..."

TRAITS

Doesn't listen	Competitive	Dismissive
Condescending	Micro-manager	Pompous
Overbearing	Oblivious	Testy/Snappy
Superiority complex/Narcissism		Insensitive

POP CULTURE

Tracy Flick (Election)
Mindy Lahiri (The Mindy Project)
Miss Piggy (The Muppets)

Sarah Huckabee Sanders (Political Adviser)
Jenna Maroney (30 Rock)

CHALLENGES

The Steamroller isn't always malicious, but her intent doesn't really matter when she's inadvertently silencing others. If she doesn't let the people around her get a word in edgewise, she won't be respected.

NOTES

STEAMROLLER

TYRANT

The Tyrant is your typical mean girl, Queen Bee. She's rude, catty, and loves to tear other women down. She can be a bully and is super judgmental. She uses sarcasm for plausible deniability when she's being a jerk. She wields ostracism as a weapon in order to exclude and punish those she's displeased with. She tends toward clique-ish behavior and can be hostile. She generally avoids communication, unless she sees an opportunity to be snarky.

The Tyrant isn't interested in helping others make progress and is liable to sabotage anyone in her way. This archetype is most associated with Toxic Bitch behavior.

MOTTO

"I'm going to crush you."

TRAITS

Rude/Catty	Hardened	Temperamental
Arrogant	Domineering	Secretive
Manipulative		Demeaning/Uses humiliation

POP CULTURE

Heather Chandler (Heathers)
Regina George (Mean Girls)
Miranda (The Devil Wears Prada)
Santana Lopez (Glee)

Endora (Bewitched)
Elektra (Pose)
Scarlett O'Hara (Gone With the Wind)
Joan Crawford (Actress)

CHALLENGES

Everyone around the Tyrant feels awful, demeaned, and degraded. She's super toxic and, frankly, nobody likes her, but they do fear her. That may be a strength or a weakness depending on your viewpoint.
(I see it as weakness.)

NOTES

TYRANT

BOLD
BADASS
ARCHETYPES

ADVOCATE

The Advocate is polite and principled and gains her strength from knowing she's doing the right thing. She rises up and makes her voice heard in service of fighting for herself or, even more likely, others. The Advocate is very matter-of-fact with strong argumentative skills, and she tends to have an academic or professional background. Generally she's very even-keeled, but she can get heated when she feels that something important is being overlooked.

The Advocate can be a great leader and tends to take a collaborative approach. She isn't a leader for power's sake; she genuinely wants to help. She can become ferocious when the situation (or her knowledge and expertise) is being inappropriately dismissed, which then requires her to assert herself. It's very important to her to "do the right thing," and she feels very integrity driven.

MOTTO

"I fight for others, so you won't silence me."

TRAITS

Polite, tactful, formal
Principled
Chooses her battles

Integrity-driven
Otherwise mild-mannered
Does the "right thing" even when it's
the hard thing

Honest
Straightforward
Academic

POP CULTURE

Alice Walker (Poet and Activist)
Jane Fonda (Actress and Activist)
Supergirl (DC Comics)
Leslie Knope (Parks and Recreation)

Gloria Steinem
Clair Huxstable (The Cosby Show)
Julia Sugarbaker (Designing Women)
Laverne Cox (Actress and Advocate)

AFFIRMATIONS

What I fight for is righteous, I am a champion for others.
I build a habit of speaking up for myself.
Confidence is strength.
My voice is my power.

CHALLENGES

She's often underestimated, and because she's polite she can be misunderstood as a bit of a Pollyanna. Then when her ferociousness comes out, the people around her are confused and taken aback. This is a classic case of how anytime a woman steps "out of line" the perception of her might move into bitch territory. Usually she's really pleasant, so when she sets a boundary in any way, people start to think she's being bitchy.

TOXIC POTENTIAL

Fanatic / Steamroller

ADVOCATE

DEALING WITH MANSPLAINERS & CONVERSATIONAL BULLDOZERS

When they take a breath or pause for even a brief moment say, "Thank you," and start right where you left off when you were interrupted.

SETTING PHYSICAL BOUNDARIES

Say, "I think I'm getting a cold, I wouldn't want you to catch it," (while waving hands in front of face and backing up).

NOTES

WARRIOR

The Warrior is a fierce fighter and will use whatever tools are necessary and available to speak up and speak out. She defends herself and others and can be ruthless if the situation calls for it. She is vigilant, tireless, and unwilling to tolerate any bullshit from the world around her. She often has one or more specific convictions that she will uphold intensely.

The Warrior can wield anger like a sharp knife and can be impatient with those who would rather take a more diplomatic approach. She doesn't have time to play at politics; her focus is on resisting being silenced and being a force for change. She sticks up for what she believes in, no matter the cost or the consequences.

MOTTO

"I will unapologetically do whatever I need to do."

TRAITS

Fierce
Tireless/relentless
Vigilant

Passionate
Intensely convicted
Persistent/Perseverent
Committed to a cause

Action-driven
Brave/Proud
Fiercely loyal

POP CULTURE

Jessica Jones (Marvel)
Blanca (Pose)
Gemma (Sons of Anarchy)

Annalise Keating (How to Get Away with Murder)
Arya Stark (Game of Thrones)
Megan Rapinoe

AFFIRMATIONS

I command respect.
My convictions are worth sticking up for.
My principles are more important than others' comfort.
I am fierce, and that is good.

CHALLENGES

Her intensity can easily lead her into Tyrant mode. She's willing to do anything (seriously, almost anything) to fight for what she believes is right. She can get impatient working within the system and lash out at her own allies.

TOXIC POTENTIAL

Fanatic / Tyrant

DEALING WITH MANSPLAINERS & CONVERSATIONAL BULLDOZERS

Interrupt them and say, "I appreciate your enthusiasm but I'm going to finish my thoughts before we move on."

SETTING PHYSICAL BOUNDARIES

Extend your hand and say, "I prefer a handshake."

NOTES

The Queen is aloof, remote, and self-contained, three traits that are often misunderstood as being snobby or unfriendly. She is a woman of few words and doesn't feel the need to comfort others with inconsequential chatter. A definite introvert, she can tend to be a bit of a loner.

When she does talk, she's thoughtful and direct and expresses her deep, meaningful beliefs. The Queen is a quiet powerhouse who can assert her beliefs without raising her voice or getting all worked up.

MOTTO

"I don't need to entertain you. I'll speak when I'm ready."

TRAITS

Enigmatic	Self-contained	Observant
Dignified	Woman of few words	Contemplative
Aloof, remote	Diplomatic	Imposing

POP CULTURE

Melinda May (Agents of SHIELD)
Letty Ortiz (Fast and the Furious)
Sansa Stark (Game of Thrones)
Furiosa (Mad Max: Fury Road)

Angelina Jolie
Lady Gaga
Anna Wintour
Rihanna

AFFIRMATIONS

It's okay to be quiet.
Direct communication is effective communication.
My dignity is my strength.
I weigh my words before speaking.

CHALLENGES

She can appear *too* mysterious and seem completely unknowable. Others are intimidated by her quietness. She can be seen as an "ice queen," and that can make her both feel and appear isolated.

TOXIC POTENTIAL

Tyrant

DEALING WITH MANSPLAINERS & CONVERSATIONAL BULLDOZERS

Make eye contact and say evenly, "I believe it's still my turn. Please let me speak before you share your thoughts."

SETTING PHYSICAL BOUNDARIES

Stand up straight, maybe even lean back ever so slightly to indicate you're not interested, and say, "It's a pleasure to meet you."

NOTES

The Boss's confidence is rooted in her competency, which others often find threatening. She's sharp and no-nonsense and uses hierarchy to support her natural leadership skills. She might be described as cold or heartless, but really she's focused on efficiency and achievement and doesn't waste time with small talk or small ideas.

The Boss believes in establishing protocols and executing best practices and processes. She expects those around her to fulfill their commitments and isn't interested in excuses or molly-coddling anyone, whether professionally or personally.

---------------------------- **MOTTO** ----------------------------

"Because I said so..."

---------------------------- **TRAITS** ----------------------------

Competent, skillful
In charge
Hierarchal

Collaborative
Brusque/No-nonsense
Enforces protocols
Accomplished

Action-driven
Authoritative
Assumes Leadership Easily

POP CULTURE

Captain Janeway (Star Trek)
Christina Yang (Grey's Anatomy)
Jessica Pearson (Suits)
Olivia (Scandal)

Kamala Harris
Martha Stewart
Hillary Clinton

AFFIRMATIONS

I have earned the respect that I expect.
My skills are useful and important and deserve to be valued.
My high standards are what get things done.
I embrace my leadership position.

CHALLENGES

She can forget that the "small talk" that she hates is actually pretty important to relationship building. Her impatience with social niceties can backfire. She's confident with leadership and is ambitious, which can be seen as negative traits in a woman specifically.

TOXIC POTENTIAL

Steamroller / Tyrant

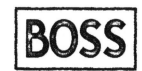

DEALING WITH MANSPLAINERS & CONVERSATIONAL BULLDOZERS

Hold your hand up in the stop motion and say,
"Just a moment. Before you jump in, I'm going to finish this thought."

SETTING PHYSICAL BOUNDARIES

As soon as you see them coming in for a hug, wordlessly extend your hand for a handshake and put a hand on their shoulder or elbow in order to help control the distance between you.

The Rebel embraces her originality and sees herself as a trailblazer. She uses unapologetic charm and wit to get her point across and never backs down from a challenge. She's often seen as "cool" and quite obviously marches to the beat of her own drum.

The Rebel is blunt and independent and doesn't respect authority for authority's sake. She understands that others may misunderstand her intent, but that doesn't slow her down or stop her from pursuing her passions.

MOTTO

"I'm doing my own thing. You can come with or get out of the way."

TRAITS

Blunt	Pioneering	Rebellious
Self-possessed	Charming	Edgy
Trailblazing	Influential	Outspoken

POP CULTURE

Angela Davis

P!nk

Emma Gonzalez

Frida Kahlo

Margaret Cho

Blanche Devereaux (Golden Girls)

Roxane Gay

Lizzo

Natalie Wynn (ContraPoints)

Veronica Mars (Veronica Mars)

Pippi Longstocking (Pippi Longstocking)

AFFIRMATIONS

I blaze my own trail.

Big things happen outside the box.

I'm bold and outspoken. I'm fierce and fearless.

My actions create my successes.

CHALLENGES

She's outside of the box but still in the system. The Rebel can struggle with still wanting to be seen as likable, so she can feel conflicted about speaking out more firmly.

TOXIC POTENTIAL

Steamroller / Tyrant

DEALING WITH MANSPLAINERS & CONVERSATIONAL BULLDOZERS

Lean forward with strong eye contact and say,
"I'm being cut short here. Please let me complete my thought, thanks."

SETTING PHYSICAL BOUNDARIES

Give them a high five!

NOTES

ROGUE

The Rogue is the edgiest and most intense profile. She's revolutionary, radical, and incredibly sharp-tongued. She doesn't care at all for social niceties and feels it's a waste of time to cater to the unenlightened. She probably enjoys vulgarity (in public or private or both). She really doesn't care if others find her likable, because she ferociously believes in what she's saying or doing.

The Rogue wears the "bitch" label with pride. Her philosophy is, "If you can't stand the heat, get out of the kitchen," and she refuses to minimize herself for the comfort of others. She is a truth-teller even when it's hard, and she will not just speak truth to power, but shout it.

MOTTO

"I don't care if you like me, but you'll hear what I have to say."

TRAITS

Unorthodox	Truth-teller	Takes no prisoners
Radical/Non-conformist	Anti-establishment	Unapologetic
Sharp-tongued/snarky	Anti-authority	Hard-nosed

POP CULTURE

Madonna
Nicki Minaj & Lil' Kim
Sandra Bernhard
Maxine Waters
Alexandria Ocasio-Cortez

Pam DeBeaufort (True Blood)
Cookie (Empire)
Margo (The Magicians)
Faith (Buffy the Vampire Slayer)

AFFIRMATIONS

My sense of self is formidable.
I am a force of nature.
My intensity is unapologetic.
I don't speak, I roar.

CHALLENGES

The Rogue can have a hard time working with others and is more of a one-woman show than a collaborator. Her sharp edges can be off-putting, and her impatience can reach toxic levels. She can seem hard as nails but might secretly be sensitive. She naturally challenges authority and that can undermine her progress. When she is really fired up she can be like a bull in a china shop.

TOXIC POTENTIAL

Fanatic / Steamroller / Tyrant

DEALING WITH MANSPLAINERS & CONVERSATIONAL BULLDOZERS

Interrupt them and say, "I wasn't done talking," and just keep right on
making the point you were making.

SETTING PHYSICAL BOUNDARIES

The Duck and Dodge will definitely get the point across. Physically moving around and away from their
outstretched arms while saying something like, "I'm not a hugger!" is direct and likely unforgettable.

Ok, so now that you've read through all the archetypes, which ones do you feel most connected to and why?

CORE
This is your most natural archetype. The one that most deeply resonates with when you read it and think, "Yep, that's me." Your core profile is who you are at your baseline, when you're happy and confident.

SECONDARY
Your secondary archetype is the one you can also see yourself in, but not as frequently. It also comes pretty naturally to you (or you've learned to work at it and make it happen).

ASPIRATIONAL
We all have traits that we would like to improve, or at least have access to, and your aspirational archetype includes those elements. In a later chapter, we'll discuss how to strengthen those traits within yourself.

SITUATIONAL
This is the archetype (or multiple archetypes) that you can draw on depending on the situation. At work, in public space, with friends or family—each can present different requirements for the way you communicate and handle yourself.

TOXIC
There's no shame in the fact that we're not always at our best. We're only human, and sometimes that means we slide into toxic territory, especially when we're feeling the need to defend ourselves. This is the archetype that you're most likely to embody as a coping mechanism if you're upset, stressed, or triggered.

YOUR FIVE ARCHETYPES

Ok, so now that you've read through all the archetypes, which ones do you feel most connected to and why?

CORE

_____
_____
_____

SECONDARY

_____
_____
_____

ASPIRATIONAL

_____
_____
_____

SITUATIONAL

_____
_____
_____

TOXIC

_____
_____
_____

TAKE ACTION:
WHICH BADASS OR BITCH (OR BOTH) ARE YOU?

Now that you've had time to get up close and personal with each archetype, it's time to think through which traits you already embody, which ones you aspire to, and which ones, if any, you want to tone down.

Thinking through these traits should help you become aware of any toxic tendencies while celebrating the badass you are.

1

Make a list of how you see yourself, and remember that you are the one who defines yourself.

2

But as we've mentioned, self-awareness is important for every kind of badass. Make a list of how you think others see you.

3

On both lists, put a check mark next to the traits you think are accurate and an X next to the ones that don't feel accurate.

4

Now, circle the traits (accurate or not) that you want to embody, and add any others you'd like to develop.

TAKE ACTION:
WHICH BADASS OR BITCH (OR BOTH) ARE YOU?

HOW DO OTHERS SEE YOU?	HOW DO YOU SEE YOURSELF?

GO DEEPER:
WHICH BITCHES & BADASSES DO YOU KNOW?

It's natural to start putting the women you know into different archetypes, too. In this blank grid, add the names of women you know under the archetypes that best describe them (their core archetypes).

ADVOCATE	WARRIOR	FANATIC

QUEEN	BOSS	STEAMROLLER

REBEL	ROGUE	TYRANT

---------- PRIORITY ASSESSMENT TOOL ----------

The simple fact is that certain people's opinions should have more weight than some other people's opinions in your life. That's not a rude thing; that's a survival thing.

Here are some questions to consider when evaluating someone's opinion of you, whether it's a colleague, family member, or friend.

Does this person have power over my life?
- ○ A: Not at all
- ○ B: Only in certain settings
- ○ C: Yes, significant power

Is this relationship important to me?
- ○ A: Not at all
- ○ B: In some ways
- ○ C: Yes, very

Is this relationship necessary?
- ○ A: Nope
- ○ B: Sometimes I think so
- ○ C: Yes definitely

Do I care about this person's opinion of me?
- ○ A: Not a bit
- ○ B: In certain situations
- ○ C: Yes, very much

Is this a short term or long term relationship?
- ○ A: Very short-term
- ○ B: We'll have to interact fairly regularly for a while
- ○ C: Long-term

Are they educated on the subject?
- ○ A: They have no idea what they're talking about
- ○ B: They know about as much as I do
- ○ C: They're experts

Are they offering any constructive feedback?
- ○ A: None
- ○ B: About some things
- ○ C: Yes, their feedback is always constructive

Are they genuinely trying to help me/lift me/support me/build me up?
- ○ A: No
- ○ B: Sometimes
- ○ C: Always

TALLY IT UP

Pick someone that you've had a conflict with.

Answer each of the above questions, and then tally your answers.

A _____
B _____
C _____

If you answered mostly A's and B's, they aren't worth your concern.
If you answered mostly B's and C's, it may be worth trying to find a solution.

Did they end up being worth considering? Then let's consider the consequences of what would happen if this person thinks you're being a toxic bitch.

What would happen if _____ thought
I was being a Toxic Bitch?

_____
_____
_____
_____
_____
_____
_____
_____
_____
_____
_____
_____

If, using this tool as a starting point, you've determined that the person in question has an opinion worth caring about and that the consequences of him (or her) thinking you're a bitch are significant enough to want to avoid, then it's time to have a conversation about how to create a mutually respectful relationship. Consider the power dynamics driving this person's perspective, and use that information to plan the most effective approach.

Remember, be curious, compassionate, and confident.

GO DEEPER:
GETTING COMFORTABLE WITH DISCOMFORT

A big part of ditching the Bitch Stigma and the fear of that stigma is learning to sit with the right kind of discomfort. We have to be prepared for rejection just for trying to broach a tough subject.

Preparing for rejection and sitting with discomfort are two things that are going to end up being a big part of this journey, because you will be uncomfortable.

So take a moment to reflect on how you currently handle uncomfortable situations and what changes you can make to make this part of your journey easier.

How do you currently deal with discomfort?

GO DEEPER:
GETTING COMFORTABLE WITH DISCOMFORT

Think about a time you made a big change in your life (whether you were saving money, building healthy habits, learning a new skill, or anything else). What strategies worked well for you, and how will you use that experience to inform this new initiative?

What are the first changes you're going to make on your journey to embracing your inner badass?

GO DEEPER:
GETTING COMFORTABLE WITH DISCOMFORT

Recognize your fear and discomfort, and make space for it. The more you try to push it down, the greater its hold on you will be. It's completely normal to feel fear or anxiety when you're making a change in your life, but you have the choice to take action anyway.

STEP ONE:

You have to change your relationship to discomfort. Instead of seeing it as something to avoid, embrace it as a sign of positive change. You have to grow and take steps to reach your goal, but they don't need to be huge steps to get you started. Make your steps manageable so that you can feel successful. Success begets success, so when you achieve something once it becomes easier and easier to achieve it again.

Start with changing the language you use about yourself. Words matter, and they're a powerful influence on how we think and what we believe. Try to cut out negative words like "can't," "difficult," and "impossible." Replace them with positive words like "try," "can," and "achieve."

Write down five negative words or sentiments you find yourself using to limit yourself. Now, write down five positive words or sentiments you'll replace them with.

1. _____ → _____
2. _____ → _____
3. _____ → _____
4. _____ → _____
5. _____ → _____

GO DEEPER:
GETTING COMFORTABLE WITH DISCOMFORT

STEP TWO:

Take action! Don't let "blender brain" (aka when your brain goes round and round on a single subject without getting anywhere) get you stuck in your own thought process. When you take action and start making changes, your own progress will inspire you to keep going.

Write down three actions you're going to take right away.

1. _____

_____

2. _____

_____

3. _____

_____

STEP THREE:

Do it all over again. This is all about building resilience. You have to believe that you will make it through the discomfort to a better life on the other side. As Thomas Jefferson allegedly said, "If you want something in life that you have never had, you will have to do something that you have never done."

In order to get comfortable feeling uncomfortable, you have to seek out things that push your limits. Repetitious expansion of your comfort zone creates opportunity for deep growth. To be truly successful, don't just tolerate discomfort, embrace it.

GO DEEPER:
GETTING TO KNOW YOUR
INNER DOOMSDAY MACHINE

The Inner Doomsday Machine is that voice in your head that is always focused on the worst possible outcome of any given action.

It's made up of your own fears and socializations, along with looping tracks from the naysayers in your life—people who talk down to you or about you.

Your Inner Doomsday Machine might be telling you how badly others are judging you. It might be telling you that others think you're toxic (even if there's no proof that they think that). Your IDM might be telling you that if you "act like a bitch," no one is going to like you or respect you. But all of those things are based on feelings, not facts. Feelings can be vague and undefined, and sometimes that's what makes them paralyzing.

Let's figure out exactly what your IDM is saying to you so we can actively counteract it. Write as many of your repetitive negative thoughts as possible.

Over the course of a week, add to this list as you notice any other catastrophic thoughts that crop up.

WHAT DOES YOUR
INNER DOOMSDAY MACHINE SAY TO YOU?

WHAT DOES YOUR
INNER DOOMSDAY MACHINE LOOK LIKE?

(use words to describe it, or draw, doodle, color, or collage)

OTHER IDM DETAILS

What does your IDM sound like? What's the tone of voice?
Does it sound like anyone you know?

When does your IDM like to chime in?
In what types of situations is your IDM the loudest?

TAKE ACTION:
SENSORY DEPRIVATION AS A TOOL FOR FOCUS

Since our Inner Doomsday Machines run constantly in the background of our minds, you probably know some of what yours says, but not everything. Making this voice concrete can be extremely helpful in combating it. If you don't usually have any visual impairment, blindfolds are a simple tool that often don't have anything to do with kink. In this case, they can help you tune into your IDM.

STEP ONE:

Either sit at a desk with a notebook and pen or at your computer (it's easier if you type). It might be helpful to have non-lyrical music in the background, or you might prefer silence to keep your focus on your inner voice.

STEP TWO:

Put the blindfold on, and take some deep breaths. This is going to feel strange at first, but let yourself sit with the discomfort (try some affirmations if you need to) and breathe through it.

STEP THREE:

Now start writing out your fears and anxieties. There's nothing fancy about this; make it as stream-of-consciousness as possible. You want to purge and document the untruths that your IDM is running in the background of your mind.

The blindfold is meant to prevent the visual cortex from registering what you're writing and kicking in with negative judgment and self-editing.

Here are some questions you can ponder during this exercise, just to get you started:

What am I afraid people will say about me?
What negative beliefs do I have about "strong women" that are holding me back?
How does my inner voice speak down to me rather than lifting me up?
How does my IDM convince me to play small rather than living a large, full life?

TAKE ACTION:
SENSORY DEPRIVATION AS A TOOL FOR FOCUS

Not into wearing a blindfold and/or writing? For those without a usual hearing impairment, you can do this as an audio and verbal combination. Try this exercise instead (or do them both if you really want to dig into these thoughts).

STEP ONE:

Go to a private place where you can be alone—somewhere you won't be disturbed and where you will be safe without your hearing and you won't worry about being heard.

STEP TWO:

Put on headphones and pick your favorite music—something that puts you in a state of flow—and turn it up as loud as you can stand without damaging your hearing.

STEP THREE:

Use an audio recorder or a voice recording app (or voice to text) on your phone to record yourself talking about the things that bother you. Speak about your fears while you're listening to loud music, so you can't hear them. Let your words flow without restricting yourself.

GO DEEPER:
WHAT WAS IT LIKE?

What was it like doing this exercise? How did it feel to express your fears without letting your brain and your IDM get in the way?

TAKE ACTION: CREATE PERSONAL AFFIRMATIONS

Quieting our doomsday monologues means changing the way we talk to ourselves. And changing the way we talk to ourselves means changing the messages we focus on. Affirmations are an old-school method that really works. If you've never tried affirmations before, you might feel silly (or maybe you've already tried them and stopped because you felt silly), but if you stick with them, you'll find they can really make an impact on your mindset.

I like to write out a handful (or more) of my favorite affirmations or quotes on index cards so that I can carry one with me for the day or flip through them if I'm feeling really anxious.

There are a few things to remember when coming up with an affirmation:

- Focus on positive words. It's better to say "I am confident" than "I don't doubt myself."
- If you're going to use a "negative" word, then make sure you include something transformative in the statement. What is the negativity turning into?
- Be sure your affirmations are true. It's ok for your affirmations to be aspirational, but if they're flat-out false, you'll find you have trouble trusting yourself. For example, "I am thin and rich!" may not be true for me, but "I am attractive and I have many resources to support me" is true, and it's a powerful affirmation.
- Make it simple and easy to remember. Don't let it be a run-on sentence. Short and sweet is the trick so that, even if you're stressed, you can recall it easily.

Here are some suggestions:

- I find personal growth in discomfort.
- I am calm.
- This discomfort will pass.
- Challenge promotes growth.
- Setting this boundary is healthy and positive.
- I am a (insert Bold Badass Archetype here).
- I have control over my thoughts and actions.
- Their opinion is irrelevant.
- I trust my assessment/intuition.

TAKE ACTION:
CREATE PERSONAL AFFIRMATIONS

If you need more suggestions, the Badass archetype profiles each include several suggested affirmations for building confidence.

(Of course, you're not limited to the affirmations associated with your primary archetype. You can also create your own or borrow from situational or aspirational archetypes at any time!)

Write out at least five affirmations that you can use to center yourself when anxiety and discomfort have become too much for you. Write them on index cards or in a notes file in your phone.

Whenever your Inner Doomsday Machine kicks on, or you need to bolster your confidence, grab your affirmations, and repeat them slowly and with intention at least five times each.

MUTUAL ADMIRATION SOCIETY

Create a Mutual Admiration Society (MAS) with a group of friends. The folks in your Mutual Admiration Society should be people you can trust to encourage you, call you out on your shit, and help you call out others on their shit. The people in your MAS need to be able to do the following:

- Listen to you vent so you can work through your frustration before you talk to the person you're having an issue with.
- Reflect back to you what they hear you saying to see if you are communicating clearly.
- Give you a compassionate critique of your behaviors or responses to tough situations.

Here are a few of the kinds of traits to look for in new members of your MAS:

- They're truth-tellers and straight-shooters. We may not always want to hear the truth, but we need someone in our life to tell it to us.
- They are strong communicators.
- They're trustworthy and aren't going to share your thoughts and experiences with other people.
- They're willing and able to invest time and energy into their relationships.
- They answer the phone when you call and respond when you text.

Traits you want in members of your MAS:

_____   _____

_____   _____

_____   _____

Are there any particular Mirror Matrix archetypes you want in your MAS?

_____   _____

_____   _____

_____   _____

MUTUAL ADMIRATION SOCIETY

When I'm feeling insecure, I'll call _____

When I've had a successful experience, I'll call _____

When I need to brainstorm, I'll call_____

When I have "blender brain," I'll call _____

When my Inner Doomsday Machine is being loud, I'll call _____

When it feels like there are no options, I'll call _____

When I need to make an important decision, I'll call_____

When I'm falling into old habits, I'll call _____

When I need a cheerleading squad and a pep talk, I'll call_____

When I need somebody to kick me into gear, I'll call_____

When I need a reminder of my goals/value/worth, I'll call _____

When I need a clear opinion on my behavior, I'll call_____

When I need to be challenged, I'll call _____

When I need to vent or rant, I'll call _____

When I need to check my privilege, I'll call_____

When I need professional advice, I'll call _____

When I need social advice, I'll call _____

When I need a distraction, I'll call_____

GO DEEPER:
ASSESS YOUR NETWORK

You may not currently have a Mutual Admiration Society, and that's okay. This exercise will help you identify ways to build your network and strengthen your relationships.

The first thing we need to do is take a look at your current network.

1

Make a list of supportive people in your life. (Sometimes we overlook encouraging people in our lives, so take some time with this one.)

2

Which of these people will be particularly supportive of the changes you are making? Reach out to them to discuss your plans.

3

Is there someone you've lost touch with who would be great for the new direction you're heading? Reach out to catch up.

4

Is there someone you interact with who is not currently in your network, but whom you admire and would like to add? Reach out to get to know them better.

GO DEEPER:
ASSESS YOUR NETWORK

Supportive people already in my life:

Friends I've lost touch with who I should get back in touch with:

Current friends I can invite to be part of my Mutual Admiration Society:

People who are not in my network but I'd like to become friends with:

GO DEEPER:
ASSESS YOUR NETWORK

Are you reading Ditch the Bitch Stigma: Embrace Your Inner Badass and want to build your Mutual Admiration Society? Or maybe you just want to start off by getting a reading buddy to go through the book with. Below you'll find three sample messages you can use as-is to send to friends, or let these samples inspire your own words to flow.

Ditch the Bitch Stigma is even more fun to read with friends so you will have someone to talk with about your rocking new confidence and communication skills. The book is chock full of ways to get interactive with the concepts, too, which are easier to do with others.

Try one of these messages or edit it to fit your own voice.

- Hey [name], I'm reading this really fantastic book called Ditch the Bitch Stigma: Embrace Your Inner Badass and I think you'd really like it. It's all about building confidence and learning how to not take any shit from anyone, but in your own style. The author gives a bunch of interactive exercises that look like fun and recommends getting a group together. Would you be interested?

- Hi [name], OMG I'm reading this awesome book and it totally made me think of you! It's called Ditch the Bitch Stigma: Embrace Your Inner Badass and it has all these useful suggestions to stop apologizing all the time (we both need to stop doing that!) and the difference between being a toxic bitch and total badass. This book would be even more fun to read together; would you want to have a mini-book club and read it with me?

- Hey [name], Have you heard of the book Ditch the Bitch Stigma: Embrace Your Inner Badass? I'm reading it and it's really good and the author talks about having a Mutual Admiration Society and it totally made me think of you. It's not about being a bitch (haha) but there are some really cool ideas about feeling more confident and not letting other people define you. The author even used to be a dominatrix! Would you want to read it together? There's a bunch of activities to do with friends and I think it would be fun.

- If you're feeling really adventurous, you can start a Meetup.com group that women in your area can join and host events like a Book Club or MAS Nights to role-play, share victories, and strategize about your current obstacles. Check out BitchStigma.com/Groups for more resources to build a local group.

GO DEEPER:
TOXIC RELATIONSHIPS

In addition to building your Mutual Admiration Society, you may need to cut people out of your network because they can't or won't support you in becoming the person you want to be.

Don't forget that toxic people often view healthy boundaries as abusive.

It's easy to keep people in our lives simply because they have always been there, and even when relationships have run their course, there is pain associated with losing people who are important to us. But if you're already experiencing pain because of the nature of an existing relationship, then ending it is more like ripping off a bandaid. It will hurt, but then you will move forward.

Have you ever had to discontinue a friendship? What happened?

GO DEEPER:
TOXIC RELATIONSHIPS

Here are some questions to ask yourself when you're trying to determine
if a friend is toxic and whether you need to move on.

- [ ] Are they overly competitive with you?

- [ ] When you share good news or progress you've made in your personal or professional life, do they immediately shift the attention back to themselves or respond negatively to what you're saying?

- [ ] Are you the one who's always reaching out or organizing times to hang out?

- [ ] Do they seem far less invested in the relationship than you are?

- [ ] Do you feel like you have to walk on eggshells around them?

- [ ] Are they prone to lashing out when they're upset or frustrated?

- [ ] Do they refuse to apologize when they've genuinely done something damaging to you or to your relationship?

- [ ] Do you feel stress, anxiety, or mistrust when you're interacting with them?

GO DEEPER:
TOXIC RELATIONSHIPS

Toxic people to reevaluate my relationship with:

Who: _____

Why: _____

_____

Who: _____

Why: _____

_____

Who: _____

Why: _____

_____

Who: _____

Why: _____

_____

Who: _____

Why: _____

_____

TAKE ACTION:
BUILD YOUR NETWORK

Once you've shored up your network by assessing who you want to keep and cutting toxic relationships, it's time to take control of who you allow in your life and start seeking out people who share your values and ambitions.

This takes effort: new relationships don't just spring up overnight. But the payoff is more than worth the investment. You need to seek out the kinds of people who will help you move forward in your life.

Places I am going to look for new friends:

Ways I'm going to make time and space for new friends:

TAKE ACTION:
TAP INTO YOUR SENSORY SPARKS

Sensory Sparks are a way to use your senses to reinforce confidence.

Our senses are an incredibly powerful influence on our internal state. We can use Sensory Sparks to create shortcuts to our most badass, confident selves. Using our senses can help us get into our subconscious to override social training.

Here are some examples of Sensory Sparks you can use:

TASTE
(honey, chocolate, salt, wine, tea)

SIGHT
(looking at a candle or photo)

TOUCH
(item to wear or stroke, such as a tiara, shoes, clothing, a stone)

SMELL
(perfume/cologne, essential oil)

SOUND
(song, album, gong, soundscapes)

MOVEMENT
(yoga, power pose, a special dance step)

On the following page, make a list of each sense and what you might be able to use as a Sensory Spark.

Once you have a small list of possibilities for each sense, circle the ones that will be the most powerful.

TAKE ACTION:
TAP INTO YOUR SENSORY SPARKS

TASTE	SIGHT	TOUCH

SMELL	SOUND	MOVEMENT

TAKE ACTION:
TAP INTO YOUR SENSORY SPARKS

From the circled options on the previous page, pick one Sensory Spark for each sense. For at least one week (preferably two or more) use the sensory spark every time you have a moment of confidence, and soon you'll be able to use that spark to summon confidence, too.

TASTE

How does it make me feel?

_____

_____

_____

_____

When will I use it?

_____

_____

_____

SIGHT

How does it make me feel?

_____

_____

_____

_____

When will I use it?

_____

_____

_____

TOUCH

How does it make me feel?

_____

_____

_____

_____

When will I use it?

_____

_____

_____

SMELL

How does it make me feel?

_____

_____

_____

_____

When will I use it?

_____

_____

_____

SOUND

How does it make me feel?

_____

_____

_____

_____

When will I use it?

_____

_____

_____

MOVEMENT

How does it make me feel?

_____

_____

_____

_____

When will I use it?

_____

_____

_____

YOUR POWER SONG & KICKASS PLAYLIST

A Power Song is a song that tends to have a fast or uplifting beat that triggers a powerful, confident mindset in you every time you listen to it. Every person is going to get inspired by the style of music they feel most connected to. Country, classical, hip-hop, pop, or rock (just to name a few) are all legitimate choices, what matters most is how the songs make you feel.

Like all trigger development, the key is to listen to the song both when you need a pickup and when you're already feeling big and powerful. By listening to your Power Song when you're already feeling powerful, you'll learn to associate that song with that state of mind. Then, when you're needing to spark that headspace, you can play the Power Song (or Power Playlist) and it will help you return to that state.

SUGGESTED SONGS

Good as Hell — Lizzo

Freedom — Beyonce

Golden — Jill Scott

Roar — Katy Perry

Eye of the Tiger — Survivor

Titanium — Sia

Unstoppable — Sia

Ladies First — Queen Latifah

Sorry Not Sorry — Demi Lovato

Shake it Off — Taylor Swift

Fight Song — Rachel Platten

Champion - Bishop Briggs

TAKE ACTION:
ROLE-PLAY DIFFICULT CONVERSATIONS

We've all heard the phrase "Practice Makes Perfect," but I want to adapt it to "Practice Makes Proficient" because perfection is not what we're looking for. By using practice to make ourselves more comfortable, we become more proficient in speaking up, even in imperfect ways.

Practicing will help you in three significant ways:

1
You'll build confidence by working through scenarios ahead of time.

2
You'll improve your reflexes so that, when a "real-life" situation comes up, you won't need as much time to process what's happening and you'll be able to respond immediately.

3
You'll literally change your brain.

One of the most effective ways we can practice is through role-playing difficult situations or conversations—that is, acting them out in a safe space with people we trust in order to get comfortable asking for what we need, setting boundaries, or taking up space.

TIPS FOR ROLEPLAY

Role-play is when you "play" with new concepts based on roles you are choosing to embody. These roles can be amplifications of a part of yourself, or they can be entirely concocted personas.

We get this picture of ourselves, and sometimes in order to get out from underneath that, we have to pretend to be someone we're not with characteristics that aren't yet authentic for us. We get trapped in the role that we think we're supposed to play, and that makes it hard to do certain activities. But when we "become" someone else, we can explore new boundaries—we can fake it till we are it.

The better you get at role-playing Bold Badass behaviors, the more you'll find you feel confident setting boundaries, shutting down bad behavior, or navigating situations that have traditionally been uncomfortable.

- Get over feeling silly, and give it all you've got. Roleplay isn't effective if you don't let go of your self-judgement and actually play along.

- When you're roleplaying for practice, create the bubble! This is what I call it when you agree with your partner that you're going to make your own rules, support each other, and laugh together without judgment.

- Inhabit the roleplay as much as possible. Use clothes, shoes, movement, and more to really get into your new persona.

- You can roleplay as either a persona completely different from your own, or you can simply work on tapping into a special part of yourself. Find the characteristics in the role that you relate to or can imagine yourself playing, and try to relax into it.

- Use your imagination (and maybe a few well-placed props) to turn your environment into the situation you need to make your roleplay successful. Use verbal cues to describe the "place" you are in, as that helps craft the psychological aspect of role-play as practice for "the real thing."

Imagine it until you inhabit it!

TAKE ACTION:
FIELD RESEARCH

Start by spending a week paying attention to how many times you or women around you acquiesce to make others comfortable. Make a note of every single time you see a woman agree to something she's obviously not happy with or accept something she obviously doesn't want.

GO DEEPER:
REWRITE THE SCENE

After a week of keeping track of these incidents, go back through and consider how that woman (or you) could've responded differently. What are the words that could've been said instead? Once you start seeing all the ways women stifle ourselves, it's impossible to unsee.

TAKE ACTION:
PRACTICE BEING A BADASS

Once you've become used to paying attention, at least twice a week, for the next three weeks, choose low or no-pressure situations where you can practice feeling like a badass. Stop a good friend when she accidentally interrupts you at lunch. Roleplay a heated conversation with a colleague to work out the best way to stand your ground. After each session, write down or record a few thoughts about how it felt to test out your new confidence tools.

What happened? _____
How did it feel? _____

What happened? _____
How did it feel? _____

What happened? _____
How did it feel? _____

What happened? _____
How did it feel? _____

What happened? _____
How did it feel? _____

What happened? _____
How did it feel? _____

GO DEEPER:
HOW DO YOU SPEAK UP & SET BOUNDARIES?

A big part of embracing your inner badass is learning to be comfortable telling others no. Whether you need them to let you finish speaking or to back away and give you space, setting boundaries is important, but it's not easy. Take some time to reflect on how often and easily you set boundaries for yourself.

What did you do this week to set your verbal boundaries?

What did you do this week to set your physical boundaries?

GO DEEPER:
HOW DO YOU SPEAK UP & SET BOUNDARIES?

Did you need to use situational or aspirational archetypes this week?
What happened?

Was there a time that you wanted to speak up but didn't? If so, describe
what happened and what you'd like to do differently next time.

TAKE ACTION:
BUILDING A REWARD SYSTEM

Making change can be difficult, and it's important to find inspiration to stay committed even when the change is taking time.

While many folks think that intrinsic motivation is the ideal, I'm a fan of using extrinsic motivation to get things going. Having something tangible that we enjoy as a reward for exploring difficult behavior gives us something to hold onto until that intrinsic motivation kicks in once we've experienced some progress.

There are a few things to keep in mind when you're building a reward system:

1

It must be truly motivational. If it's something that you'll have anytime (like a candy bar or a talk with a friend), it's not sufficiently motivational to help you get over the hump of not wanting to do it.

2

The reward can't be harmful or counterproductive.

3

It's best if it's something that you can do yourself rather than depending on someone else to provide the reward.

GO DEEPER:
INCENTIVIZING CONFIDENCE

What are you going to do to reward yourself when you when you change your behavior, before you actually get to the outcome?

What can you do to continue to keep yourself inspired to work on these changes?

What self care behaviors that you can rely on when the going gets tough.

TAKE ACTION:
KEEP TRACK FOR A MONTH

Even as an adult, I'm a big fan of gold stars.

They're a great little extrinsic motivator to keep you excited as you work toward the bigger reward you've chosen for yourself. So I've included three month's worth of stars for you to track your progress in this workbook.

Choose one or two actions you want to take to improve your communication or confidence skills. You can choose one skill per month to track, or choose a couple and use different colored stars when you put them into practice.

Color in each star at the end of the day once you've done the new thing. Or even better, buy a set of inexpensive gold star stickers and use those to acknowledge your daily success.

Once you've reached the goal you've set for yourself,
reward yourself as planned!

GOLD STAR TRACKING

GOAL

_____

_____

_____

_____

GOLD STAR TRACKING

GOAL

GOLD STAR TRACKING

GOAL

Let's start with some questions designed to get you thinking about every aspect of your Most Confident Self. Answer each question as thoroughly as you can. Once you're done, put it aside for three or four days, and then come back to it to add any other thoughts you've had.

What does your Most Confident Self look like?
(Color, collage, or use other creative skills here.)

YOUR MOST CONFIDENT SELF

Think about what your life would be like if the Bitch Stigma wasn't holding you back. What would you do differently? How would you communicate with others on an everyday basis?

YOUR MOST CONFIDENT SELF

What are the words you want associated with your MCS?

How do you want others to perceive you?

How do you want to feel inside?

YOUR MOST CONFIDENT SELF

How will you move? How does your walking style or stride change? What kind of eye contact do you use? What does your personal space bubble look like? How do you enforce that space?

YOUR MOST CONFIDENT SELF

Do you dress differently or change your appearance in any way? Are different colors attractive to you? What does the style of your clothes look like?

YOUR MOST CONFIDENT SELF

How will you interact differently with people in various aspects of your life? Work? Friends? Family? Intimate partners?

_____
_____
_____
_____
_____
_____
_____
_____
_____
_____
_____
_____
_____
_____
_____
_____
_____
_____
_____
_____
_____

WHO INSPIRES YOU?

It's important for women not to feel like we have to fit ourselves into any one certain archetype. So let's look at some different role models we can look to as inspiration. We can start with the examples listed in each Bold Badass archetype.

Next, make a list of the powerful women who inspire you. You can draw from the archetype profiles or you can brainstorm your own. Underneath each name, write out the traits you want to internalize. List every reason you can think of for why you look up to each person. Now go through and circle the top five or six characteristics that you want to bring into your life.

How can you start to develop these traits in yourself?
Think of the sensory sparks, role-play opportunities & practice scenarios that can help you get started.

Role Model: _____
Traits You Admire:
- _____
- _____
- _____
- _____

Role Model: _____
Traits You Admire:
- _____
- _____
- _____
- _____

Role Model: _____
Traits You Admire:
- _____
- _____
- _____
- _____

Role Model: _____
Traits You Admire:
- _____
- _____
- _____
- _____

125

MOST CONFIDENT SELF PROFILE

In each of these sections, write why the profile resonated for you.

Core Archetype:

Secondary Archetype:

Aspirational Archetype(s):

Situational Archetype(s):

Sensory Sparks:

Sight:

Scent:

Sound:

Touch:

Taste:

Movement:

MOST CONFIDENT SELF PROFILE

Mottos or Quotes: _____

_____

_____

Theme Songs: _____

_____

_____

Body Language: _____

_____

_____

Ideal Traits: _____

_____

_____

Role Models: _____

_____

_____

Affirmations: _____

_____

_____

Don't let your MCS Profile stagnate in a book or a drawer. Keep it where you can reference it often (there's a downloadable version when you sign up for the Bitch Stigma Library at BitchStigma.com/Library). You can add to it and edit it anytime and let it remind you of the different ways you can access and express your confidence and power.

TAKE ACTION:
BUILD A VISION BOARD

Now, let's make your MCS even more tangible. You can do this while you're filling out your profile if you need some inspiration, or after you're done, when you're ready to bring your ideas to life. A vision board is a physical reminder of who you are and who you want to become. It's time to take the brainstorming, writing, and reflecting from our work throughout this book and turn it into a visual blueprint of the self you're celebrating and creating. There's no way having some motivational quotes and pictures of far off destinations can inherently make change in your life. But they can be an excellent reminder of why you're taking action to make change. Your vision board is a place of visual inspiration and encouragement.

So let your vision board represent success, of course, but make sure its primary focus is on the actions you'll take to achieve that success. Your vision board might include pictures of women talking to each other to represent new relationships you're building or friends you need to have hard conversations with. It might include photos that represent challenging situations like team meetings or first dates that you're working to embrace. Or some of your affirmations or the Sensory Sparks you're using to help create sense memories of confidence. The beauty of a vision board is that there aren't any rules about what you can and can't include. Just be sure to focus on the effort you're making, not just the end result you're striving for. Find inspiration for your image and word choices in your role models, Mirror Matrix archetypes, sensory sparks, affirmations and mantras, plans, and goals.

WHAT YOU'LL NEED:

Sturdy paper/cardstock to use as the foundation + A glue stick
Words and images clipped from magazines or printed from online sources

Layer the images and words together on the cardstock to cover as much of the background as feels right. You can write directly on the glued images with markers and pens too. Hang the vision board somewhere you'll see it frequently. Next to your bed is ideal so you'll see it upon rising and before going to sleep. Let your eyes look over it as often as possible in order to really bury those messages into your mind.

GO DEEPER:
REFLECT ON MISCOMMUNICATIONS

Many women struggle to communicate clearly because they feel like asking for what they need, expressing their opinions, or making their frustrations known is too burdensome to others. But it's important to remember that communication is a gift, and when we express ourselves clearly and confidently, we're not only embracing our own inner badasses but we're empowering others to help us get what we need.

Think about a recent disagreement you had with a friend, colleague, or partner, or a time when your needs weren't met. Could you have communicated more clearly in that situation? How might it have gone if you had?

TAKE ACTION: JUST SAY NO

If you're someone who struggles to say no, then it's time to push outside of your comfort zone and give no a go. For the next week, whenever someone asks you to do something you really don't want to do, say no without any further explanation. Fight the urge to soften the no, and simply say, "Thank you, but no."

What happened? _____
How did it feel? _____

What happened? _____
How did it feel? _____

What happened? _____
How did it feel? _____

What happened? _____
How did it feel? _____

What happened? _____
How did it feel? _____

What happened? _____
How did it feel? _____

What happened? _____
How did it feel? _____

GO DEEPER:
IDENTIFYING YOUR SOFT LANGUAGE HABITS

One of the most common ways the Bitch Stigma affects women is in the way we communicate. Because women are often socialized to be nice and polite, we lean on "soft language" to pad our messages and protect our audiences. But it often backfires and makes us sound unconfident and in need of reassurance.

> ## Here are some examples of softening language:
>
> Apologizing all the time
>
> Being sorry for simply "taking up space"
>
> Qualifying statements with "maybe," "should we consider," or "if you think we should"
>
> Starting all sentences with "I feel" or "I think" or "I believe"
>
> Starting sentences with "Can I just say something..."
>
> Downplaying your own knowledge with "Maybe I'm wrong, but..."
>
> Saying "just" a lot ("I was just thinking," etc.)
>
> Using a lot of exclamation points, speaking in a really perky way, or making everything you say sound like a question
>
> Frequently allowing people to talk over you
>
> Ending sentences with "don't you agree?" or "what do you think?" or "if it's ok with you."

GO DEEPER:
IDENTIFYING YOUR SOFT LANGUAGE HABITS

What kind of soft language do you use most frequently?

How does it feel to imagine not using those soft language techniques anymore?

Where do you need to start with removing soft language?
In your emails? At work? Where else?

TAKE ACTION:
TAKE A SORRY DETOX

While you're working on removing soft language from your writing, practice removing it from your speech, too.

Focus on one word or phrase per week, and remove them from your vocabulary one at a time. It's a "Sorry Detox." You can even put a dollar in a jar every time you accidentally say it, then treat yourself with something fabulous once you've broken the habit. (If putting money in a jar isn't an effective or feasible reward system for you, you can personalize it to anything that will motivate you to track your behavior.)

In short, there's almost always a better option than "I'm sorry."

Here are some suggestions:

- Offer a solution: Rather than focusing on a mistake that was made, skip straight to correcting it. "I didn't include this information in the last email. You can find additional details below."
- Shift from regret to gratitude: Instead of "I'm so sorry this is late!" say, "Thank you for your patience."
- Focus on solidarity, if that's what you mean: Rather than "I'm sorry you're going through that," say, "That sounds so frustrating. I'm not sure how to help, but I'm here for you."

Other phrases that can come in handy when avoiding excessive apologizing:

- Good catch, I'll make the updates/changes.
- Thanks for bringing this to my attention.
- Excuse me, pardon me, or go ahead.
- Could you clarify...
- I have a question about...
- Thank you for the invitation, but I'm not able to make it.
- I appreciate the input, but we need to move onto the next point.

----- TAKE ACTION: SPEAK WITH STRENGTH -----

INSTEAD OF THIS	TRY THIS	
"I'm so sorry, I can't believe I messed that up!"	"Good catch! Thanks for bringing it to my attention."	"I'm glad you spotted that. I'll make the change."
"Can I just say something?"	"Here's what I think.."	[Just say it!]
[Allowing someone whose opinion you don't need to speak over you]	"Thanks for the input, but we need to move onto the next point."	"I'm confident with my decision."
"Oh I'm so sorry you're experiencing that"	"That sounds frustrating. I'm not sure how to help but I'm here for you."	"Let us know how we can support you."
"I'm sorry, I'm trying to get by."	"Can I get by real quick? Thanks!"	"Excuse me."
"Oh no, I'm so sorry but I can't do [insert anything there]"	"Thanks for the invitation but I can't make it."	"I can't take that on right now but thanks for thinking of me."
"I'm sorry, I don't understand"	"Could you clarify..."	"Let me see if I understand."
"I'm sorry I wasn't clear."	"Thanks for asking clarifying questions, here's additional information.."	"Let me put it another way."
"I'm sorry, I need you to.."	"I need you to...thanks!"	"Would it work for you to.."
"Oh I'm so sorry I'm running late, [insert lengthy excuse here.]"	"Thank you for patience.."	"I appreciate you waiting for me."

Download the printable chart at BitchStigma.com/Library and post it next to your desk as a daily reminder.

TAKE ACTION:
WRITE STRONGER EMAILS

Removing soft language from written communication has been one of the most powerful things I've done. I write something out and then I go back and remove every single apologetic-sounding phrase. I usually also have to remove a few exclamation points that I've included because I think they'll make me sound happier. Really, all they do is diminish my authority.

Stop using questions to make statements. Be declarative. Use short sentences.

STEP ONE:

Go back through the emails you've written in the last week or two. Identify places where you explicitly apologize, where you soften your language, and where you otherwise "kneecap" your writing. Make a note of what your patterns are and what you need to especially keep an eye out for as you practice communicating with more strength.

Write down the apologetic/undermining phrases you found in your recent emails.

TAKE ACTION:
WRITE STRONGER EMAILS

STEP TWO:

Now it's time to start changing your habits. This week, reread every email
before you hit send, and remove these words:

I'm sorry	Just	Maybe
Sort of	Can you (especially when you're the boss)	I hope that
Kind of	I think or In my opinion	Or whatever

There's even a Google Chrome/Gmail plug-in to help with this. "Just Not Sorry" warns you when
you write emails using words that undermine your message. Install it, and use it for two weeks.
After the two weeks are over, spend some time reflecting on the experience.

What was it like? Did using confident language become easier or more natural over time?

TAKE ACTION:
SPEAK WITH AUTHORITY

Now that you've started writing more confidently, apply the same exercise to the way you talk, and start speaking with clearer authority. Think of it as making micro-assertions. Make statements instead of asking questions. You can still be polite without speaking in a way that is overly apologetic or diminishing of yourself.

Which words, phrases, and tones will you eliminate from your vocabulary?

Which words, phrases, and tones will you replace them with?

How will you be sure you notice your self-undermining speaking habits in order to correct them?

GO DEEPER:
MANSPLAINING & CONVERSATIONAL BULLDOZERS

Mansplaining is a very specific style of communication. It's not simply anytime a man opens his mouth. Mansplaining occurs when a man speaks condescendingly to a woman under the (often incorrect) assumption that he knows more about the subject than she does, simply because he's a man. Mansplaining is specifically rooted in the power dynamics of gender.

The term "mansplaining" is pointing out an inequitable power differential that allows men to feel entitled to women's attention and dismiss their expertise. It's punching up. Other terms like "womansplaining" are punching down. They may refer to the same action, but when a woman "'splains" something, she's not doing it from the same place of social power as a man. So to put mansplaining and womansplaining on the same plain really reinforces—rather than reduces—the inequitable power differential.

Conversational bulldozing, on the other hand, is a much less intentional form of interruption that occurs when one person dominates a conversation without truly realizing what he or she is doing. Conversational bulldozers can be people of any gender. Sometimes it's motivated by obliviousness, as some people just really don't realize how much they're talking. Sometimes it's motivated by a power dynamic, as when someone consciously or unconsciously believes that the person talking is the one with the power, so they won't let anyone else get a word in edgewise. Conversational bulldozers interrupt and dominate any discussion they're a part of.

What they both have in common is a disrespect (intentional or not) to the person they're in conversation with.

GO DEEPER: MANSPLAINING & CONVERSATIONAL BULLDOZERS

Do you think that there's a difference between mansplaining and conversational bulldozing?

What are some examples of each that you've experienced?

GO DEEPER:
MANSPLAINING & CONVERSATIONAL BULLDOZERS

What do you usually do if you're being talked over
or your expertise is being ignored?

TIPS & SCRIPTS
TO STOP MANSPLAINERS &
CONVERSATIONAL BULLDOZERS

Here are some specific things to keep in mind when you need to stop a mansplainer or conversational bulldozer.

Silent protest and body language will rarely work alone. If you're with other women, help amplify what they're saying. I often use humor and a light-hearted approach with increasing firmness if they aren't receptive to the softer redirection.

"Oh yes! I'm already familiar with _____ so we can move on."

"Thanks for the info, but I have it covered!"

"Thanks, but we don't need to go any deeper into that subject."

"I appreciate you telling me about this. However, what I'm talking about is this right here."

"I'm going to finish this thought, and then I'd love to hear what you think."

"I'd really love to hear your thoughts but just give me a minute.
I want to complete this thought of mine to share with you."

"I'd love to hear what you have to say but let me finish the story and then we'll get right back to you."

"I'm gonna stop you right there."

"Hey, let me stop you there."

TAKE ACTION:
PRACTICE STRATEGIC INTERRUPTING

These phrases are particularly important to practice, so it's
time to get out there with your MAS (Mutual Admiration Society)
or in lower pressure, real life situations

(for example, with a friend rather than a work colleague).

If you're practicing with your MAS, swap back and forth so you each have a turn as the
conversational bulldozer and as the one speaking up. Try out the different phrases mentioned
in this chapter. Come up with your own and write them down. For inspiration, refer back to the Mirror
Matrix archetype profiles for examples of how every badass bitch might handle an interruptor.

I'd even recommend putting them on flashcards (either with old-fashioned index cards or an app
on your phone) so that you can read through them on a regular basis.

The more comfortable and automatic these phrases are for you,
the more easily you'll be able to use them when you need them.

GO DEEPER:
STRATEGIC INTERRUPTING

How do you feel when you interrupt people?

How does it feel when you're interrupted?

GO DEEPER:
PROTECT YOUR PERSONAL SPACE

How often do you catch yourself trying to take up as little space as possible? How often do you find others invading what little personal space you have in crowded public areas?

As we learn to become our most confident selves, we have to learn how to set physical boundaries and be comfortable taking up space.

Write about a time your personal space was violated.
What would you do differently now?

Recall a time when you intentionally took up space. How did it feel?
(If you can't recall a time, imagine what it might feel like.)

TAKE ACTION: GET BIG

List three ways you're going to practice taking up space in the next week.

You can try one strategy per day, see how it goes, and log your experiences in your journal. Use your gold stars to reward yourself when you push outside of your comfort zone.

What happened? _____
How did it feel? _____

What happened? _____
How did it feel? _____

What happened? _____
How did it feel? _____

What happened? _____
How did it feel? _____

What happened? _____
How did it feel? _____

What happened? _____
How did it feel? _____

GO DEEPER:
WHERE ARE YOU NOW?

Now that you've finished reading Ditch the Bitch Stigma and working through these exercises, it's time to reflect on the experience overall and how you plan to bring what you've learned into your everyday life.

What has your experience been with reading the book, using this workbook, and putting the suggestions into action?

Is there anything you found especially easy?
Is there anything you found especially difficult?

GO DEEPER:
WHERE ARE YOU NOW?

How did it impact your experience to do it along with your Mutual Admiration Society (if you had one)? If you went through the book alone, what do you think you could get out of it by doing it with friends?

How are you going to continue to integrate these ideas into your life?

RECOMMENDED READING

- The Secret Thoughts of Successful Women: Why Capable People Suffer From the Imposter Syndrome and How to Thrive in Spite of It, by Dr. Valerie Young
- You Just Don't Understand: Women and Men in Conversation, by Deborah Tannen
- Good and Mad: The Revolutionary Power of Women's Anger, by Rebecca Traister
- Eloquent Rage, by Brittney Cooper
- Friendships Don't Just Happen!: The Guide to Creating a Meaningful Circle of GirlFriends, by Shasta Nelson
- Unscrewed: Women, Sex, Power, and How to Stop Letting the System Screw Us All, by Jaclyn Friedman

ADD YOUR OWN

BONUS!

Remember, many of these pages are also available as printable worksheets at BitchStigma.com/library along with other fun additional resources.

READY TO TAKE ACTION?

I would love to hear how this workbook has helped you take action in your life. Which strategies have changed your life? Which theories made you see things in a new way or say "Yes!"? Email yes@bitchstigma.com to tell me how this book has inspired you to embrace your inner badass and ditch the Bitch Stigma. I'm grateful to all the women who've shared their "yes!" moments already, and I can't wait to hear yours.

HIRE ME AS A SPEAKER

Are you interested in bringing me into your organization to help your people learn how to use confidence and influence to become more effective and powerful communicators? Find more information at KaliWilliams.com

JOIN ME AT THE BADASS BREAKTHROUGH RETREAT OR IN A COACHING PROGRAM

Would you like to work with me directly? I offer one-on-one and group coaching programs as well as in-person retreats throughout the year. Find more information at BadassBreakthough.com

Made in the USA
Monee, IL
26 April 2021